CW00540903

Viola
Scales & Arpeggios
ABRSM Grades 6–8

from **2012**

Why practise scales?

Welcome to this book of scales and arpeggios for Grades 6–8 Viola. Practising scales and arpeggios plays an essential part in developing a player's skills. Time devoted to these exercises within each practice session will improve many aspects of technique, such as co-ordination, string crossing, bow control, position changes and tone production. In addition, the sense of key and pattern acquired through familiarity with scales and arpeggios has several benefits: it speeds up the learning of new pieces, builds aural awareness, increases familiarity with the geography of the instrument, and helps develop fine intonation, evenness of line and quality of tone.

For the exam

Tempo

The candidate should aim for a tempo that achieves vitality of rhythm, controlled bowing, good intonation, and a clean, sonorous tone. Slurred patterns should generally be played with the whole bow, while separately-bowed examples should be played with a smooth *détaché*, using no more than half the bow length.

The given metronome marks indicate suggested *minimum* speeds for the exam. Candidates may feel that slurred requirements become more comfortable when played at a brisker tempo than examples with separate bows, such differences in speed being dependent on factors such as size of instrument and length of bow. Experienced teachers will know what their candidates are able to achieve safely, although it is important to avoid accurate yet laboured playing which demonstrates that the pattern has been memorized but lacks the musical fluency needed for a convincing result.

Fingering

The suggested fingerings in this book are neither obligatory nor exhaustive; any practical fingering that produces a good result will be accepted in the exam. The decision as to which fingering to adopt will vary between players, taking into account ease of performance, memorability, and the importance of changing position unobtrusively, and candidates should experiment to find solutions that work for them. (Examiners will not comment on the choice of fingering, unless it interferes with the musical outcome of the performance.)

On the day

All requirements must be played from memory. Examiners will usually ask for at least one of each type of scale or arpeggio required at the grade, and will aim to hear a balance of separately-bowed and slurred requirements.

The examiner will be looking for:
- good intonation across the pitch range
- an even and positive sense of rhythm
- accurate and fluent realization of the different types of scales and arpeggios
- confident, controlled, and consistent tone
- convincing negotiation of technical challenges such as string crossing, position changing, and co-ordination.

Rhythm patterns

For major and minor scales candidates may choose between two rhythm patterns: even notes *or* long tonic.

In this book, major and minor scales are presented in even notes first, followed by the same scales using the long-tonic pattern.

(NB: This choice of rhythm pattern also applies to the double-stop scale in parallel sixths in Grade 8.)

Reference must always be made to the syllabus for the year in which the exam is to be taken, in case any changes have been made to the requirements.

Music origination by Julia Bovee
Printed in England by Caligraving Ltd, Thetford, Norfolk, on materials from sustainable sources
Reprinted in 2017

GRADE 6
SCALES even notes *or* long tonic at candidate's choice

EVEN NOTES

separate bows *and* slurred
minor scales in melodic *and* harmonic form

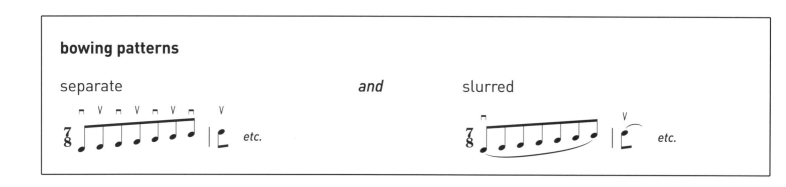

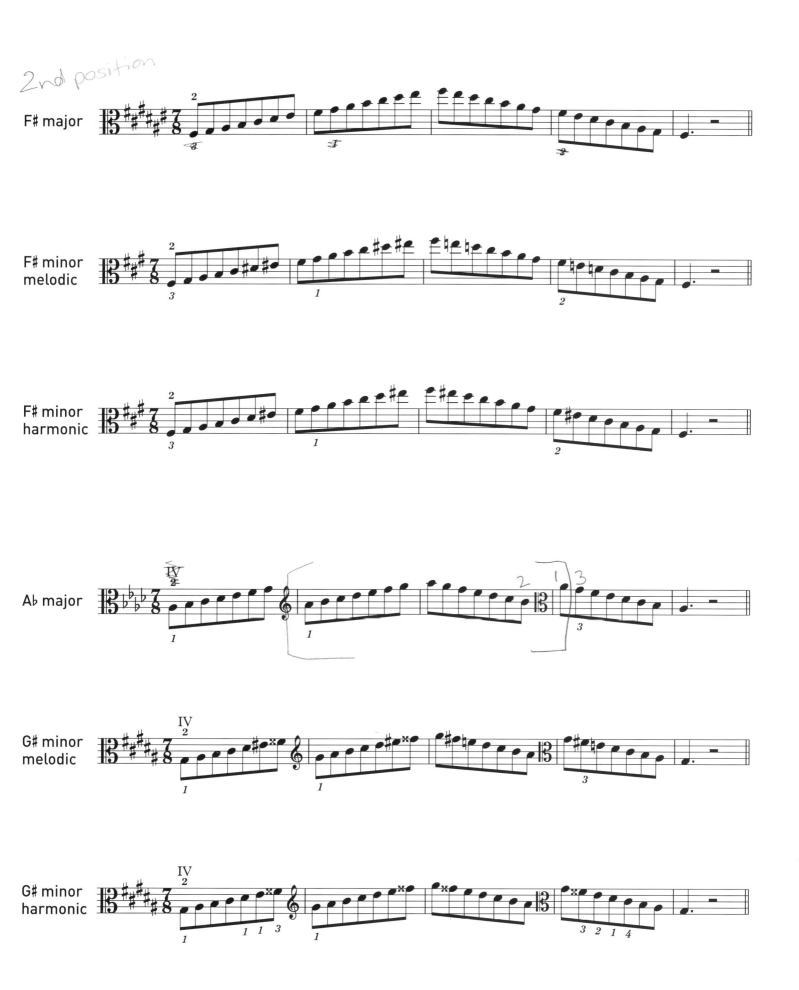

three octaves ♪ = 168 (♩ = 84)

C major

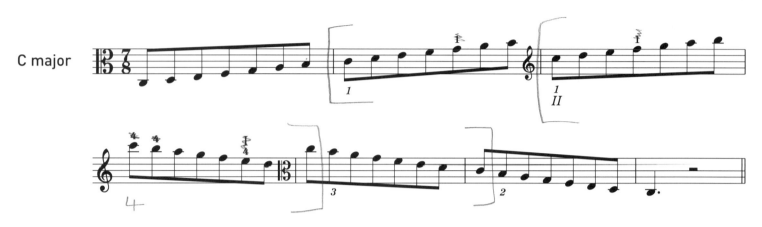

C minor
melodic

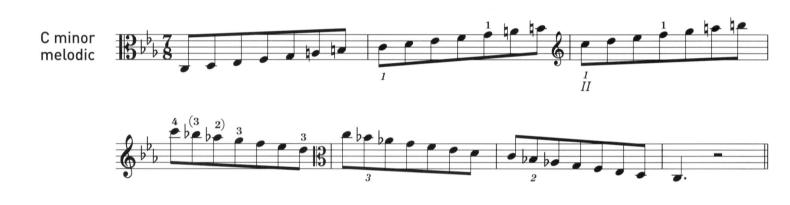

C minor
harmonic

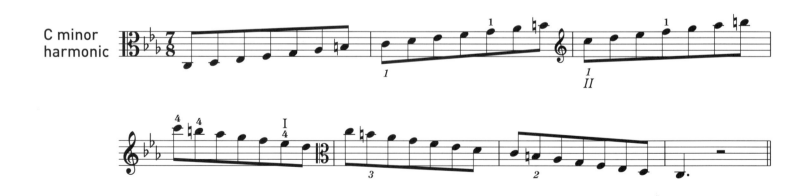

D major

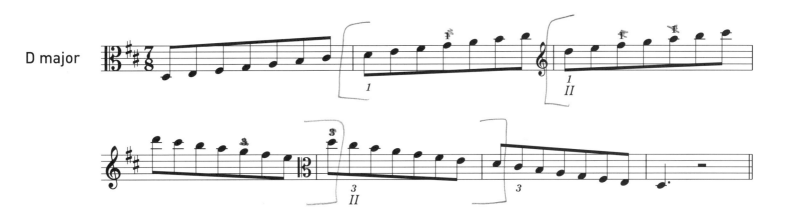

D minor melodic

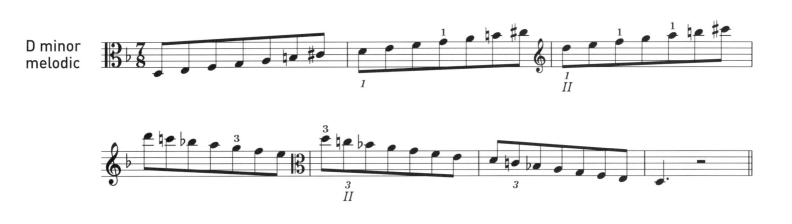

D minor harmonic

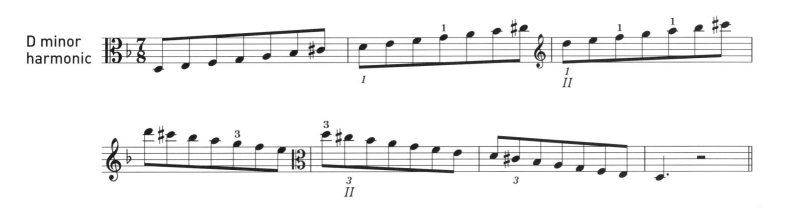

LONG TONIC
separate bows *and* slurred
minor scales in melodic *and* harmonic form

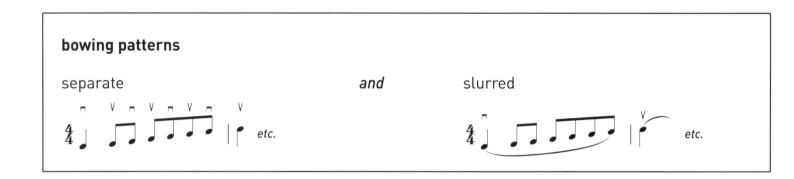

two octaves ♩ = 84

F# major

F# minor
melodic

F# minor
harmonic

Ab major

G# minor
melodic

G# minor
harmonic

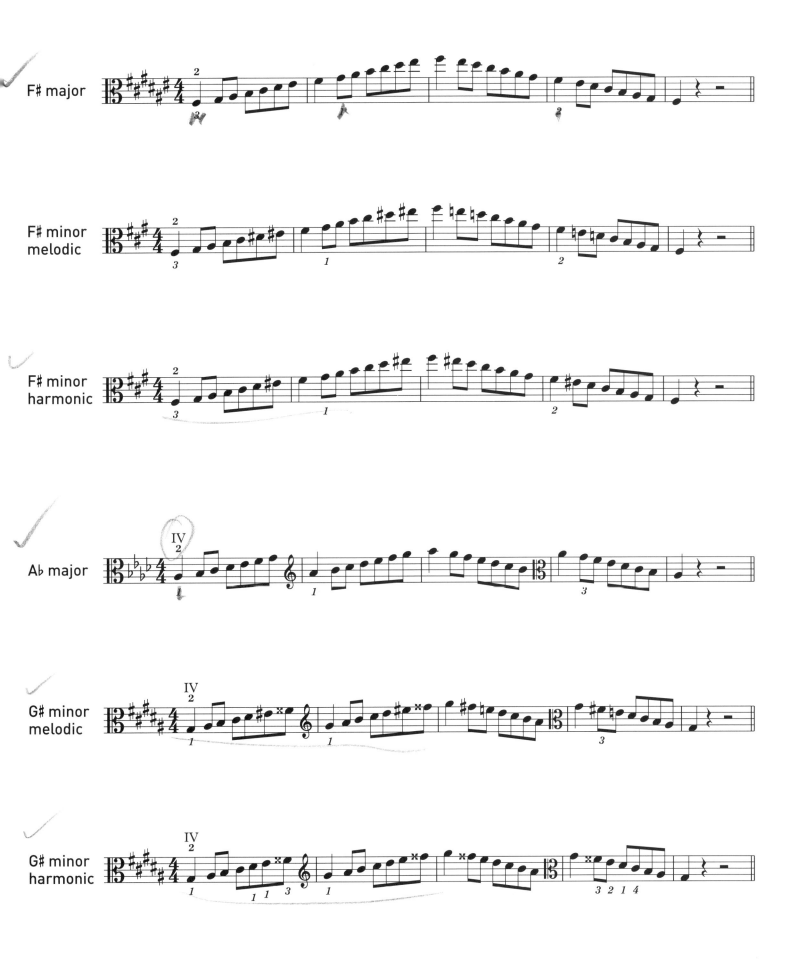

three octaves ♩ = 84

C major

C minor
melodic

C minor
harmonic

D major

D minor
melodic

D minor
harmonic

ARPEGGIOS
separate bows *and* slurred

two octaves ♩. = 42

AB 3619

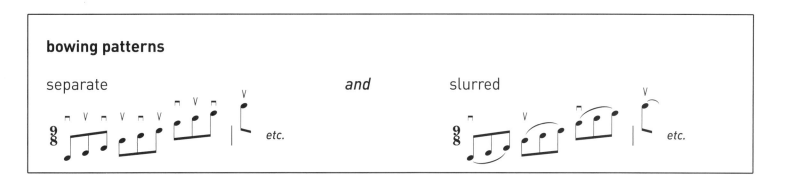

three octaves ♩. = 42

DOMINANT SEVENTHS
separate bows *and* slurred

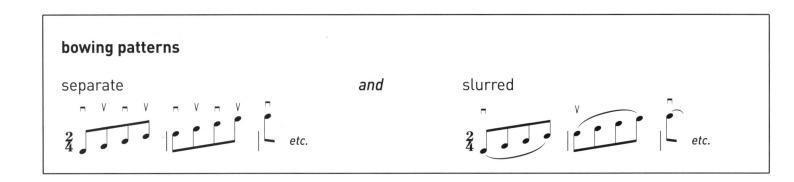

DIMINISHED SEVENTHS

separate bows *and* slurred

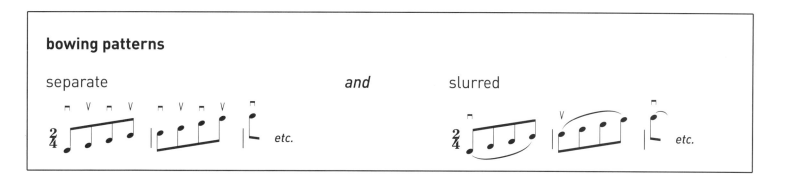

two octaves ♩ = 63

starting
on C

starting
on C#

starting
on D

For practical purposes, the diminished sevenths are notated using some enharmonic equivalents.

CHROMATIC SCALES

separate bows *and* slurred

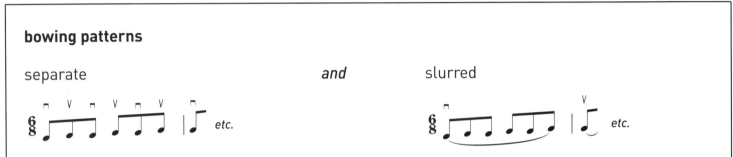

AB 3619

DOUBLE-STOP SCALE

IN BROKEN STEPS

rhythm and bowing as shown

one octave ♩ = 84

in sixths
in E♭ major

GRADE 7
SCALES even notes *or* long tonic at candidate's choice

EVEN NOTES
separate bows *and* slurred
minor scales in melodic *and* harmonic form

bowing patterns

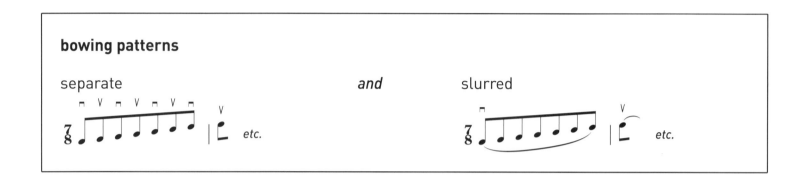

two octaves ♪ = 192 (♩ = 96)

F major

F minor melodic

F minor harmonic

AB 3619

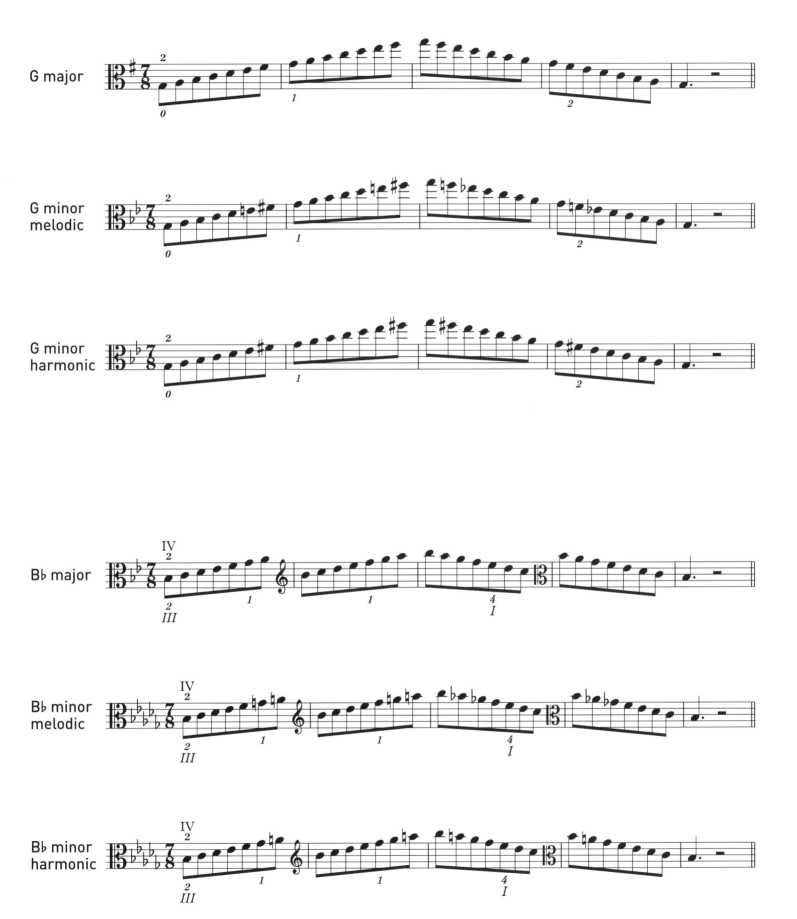

G major

G minor melodic

G minor harmonic

B♭ major

B♭ minor melodic

B♭ minor harmonic

three octaves ♪ = 192 (♩ = 96)

D major

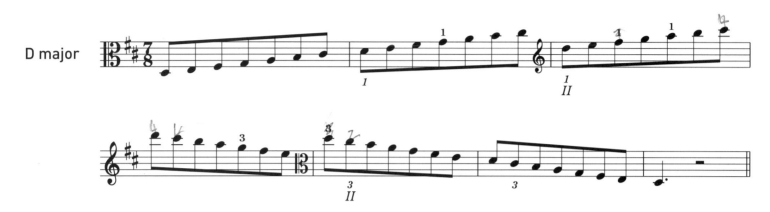

D minor
melodic

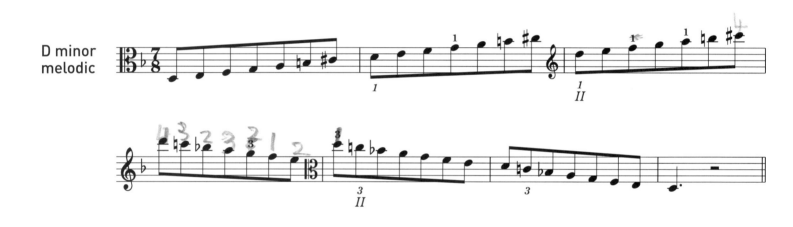

D minor
harmonic

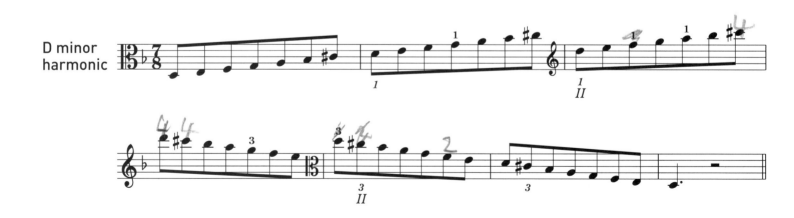

Eb major

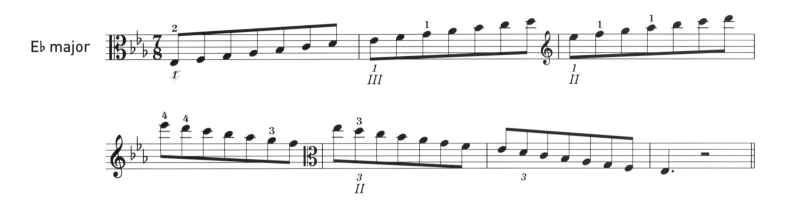

Eb minor
melodic

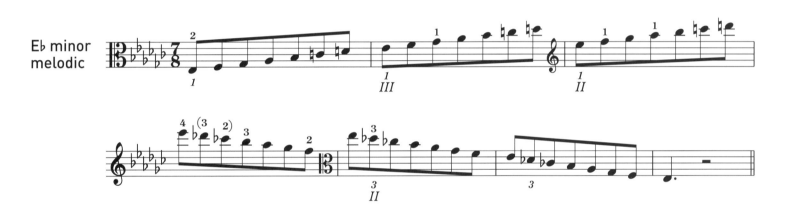

Eb minor
harmonic

LONG TONIC

separate bows *and* slurred
minor scales in melodic *and* harmonic form

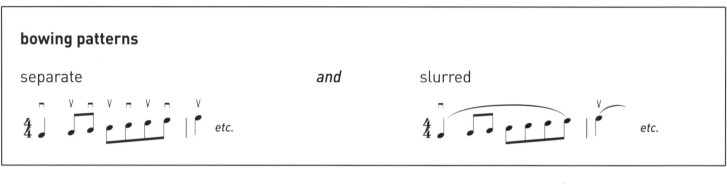

G major

G minor melodic

G minor harmonic

Bb major

Bb minor melodic

Bb minor harmonic

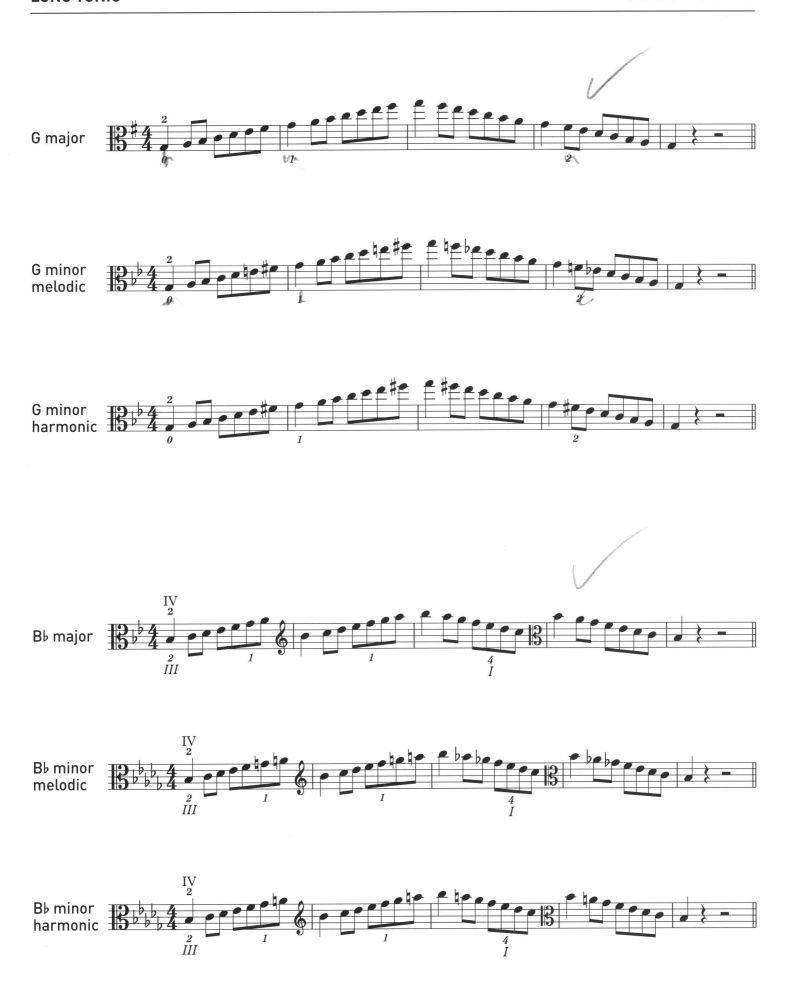

three octaves ♩ = 96

D major

D minor melodic

D minor harmonic

Eb major

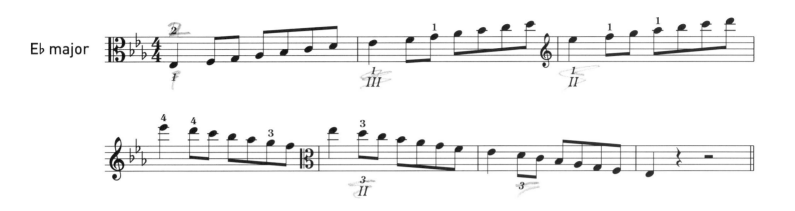

Eb minor
melodic

Eb minor
harmonic

ARPEGGIOS

separate bows *and* slurred

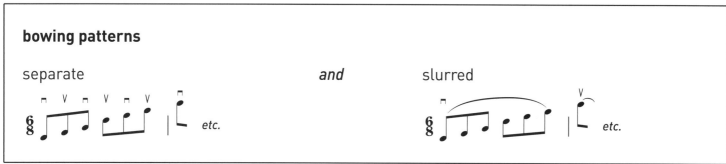

two octaves ♩. = 44

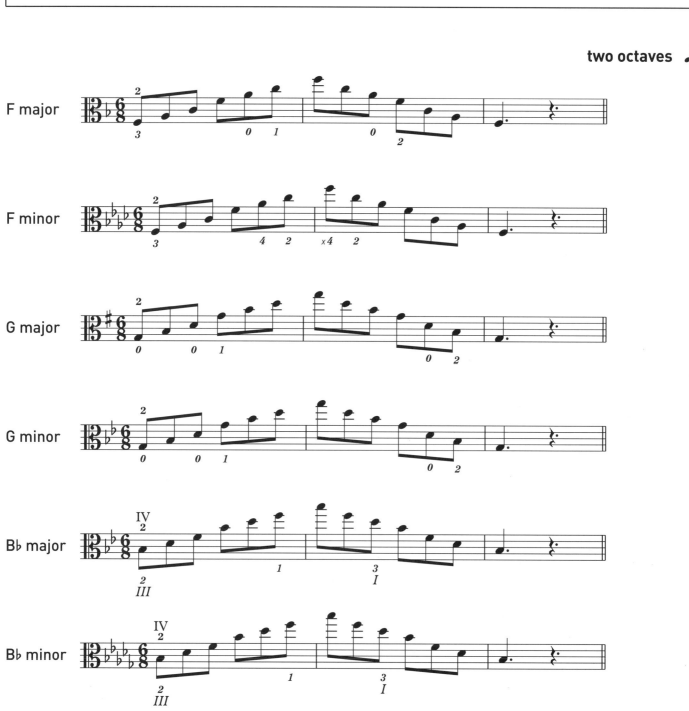

AB 3619

bowing patterns

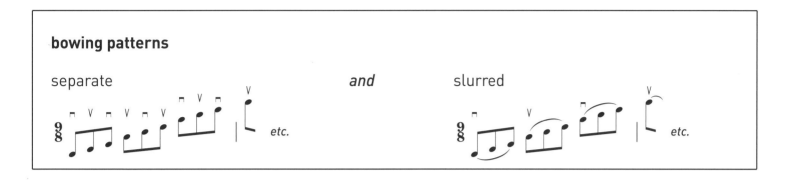

three octaves ♩. = 44

D major

D minor

E♭ major

E♭ minor

DOMINANT SEVENTHS

separate bows *and* slurred

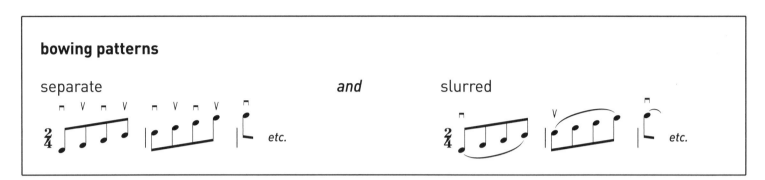

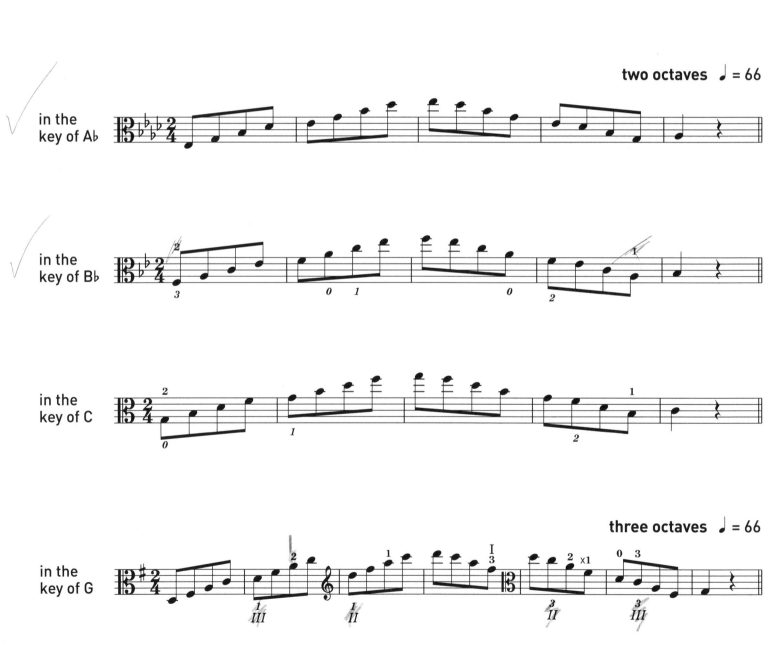

DIMINISHED SEVENTHS

separate bows *and* slurred

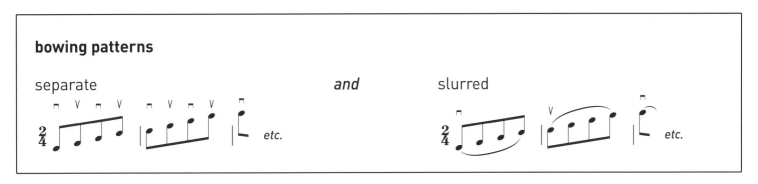

two octaves ♩ = 66

starting on E♭

starting on F

starting on G

three octaves ♩ = 66

starting on D

For practical purposes, the diminished sevenths are notated using some enharmonic equivalents.

CHROMATIC SCALES

separate bows *and* slurred

bowing patterns

separate *and* slurred

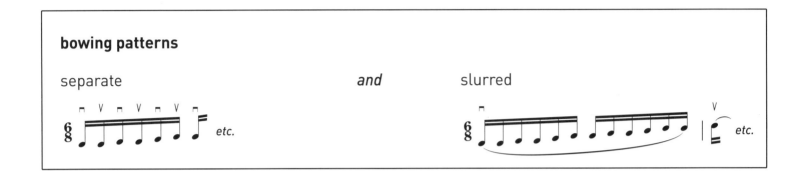

two octaves ♪ = 96

starting on E♭

starting on F

AB 3619

starting on G

three octaves ♪ = 96

starting on D

DOUBLE-STOP SCALES

IN BROKEN STEPS
rhythm and bowing as shown

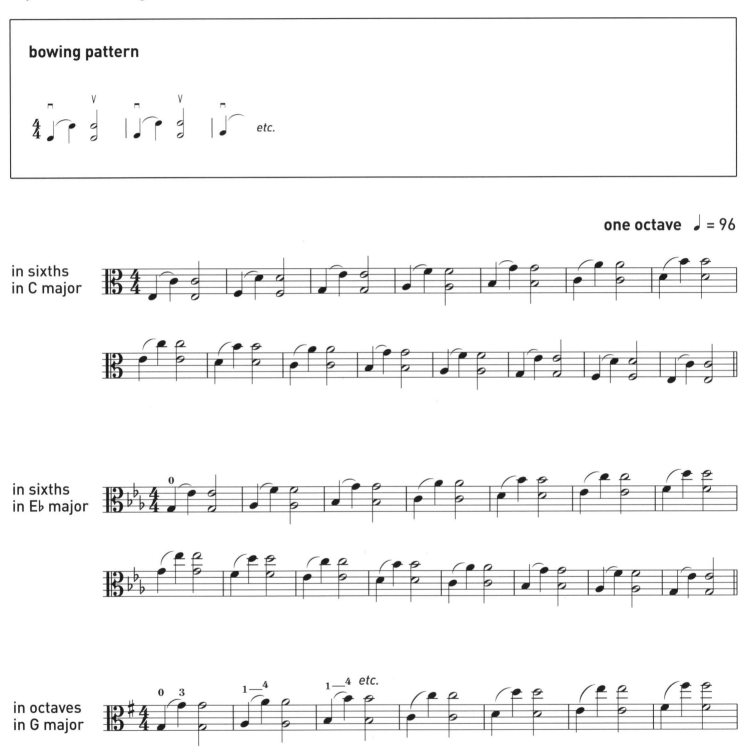

GRADE 8
SCALES even notes *or* long tonic at candidate's choice

EVEN NOTES
separate bows *and* slurred
minor scales in melodic *and* harmonic form

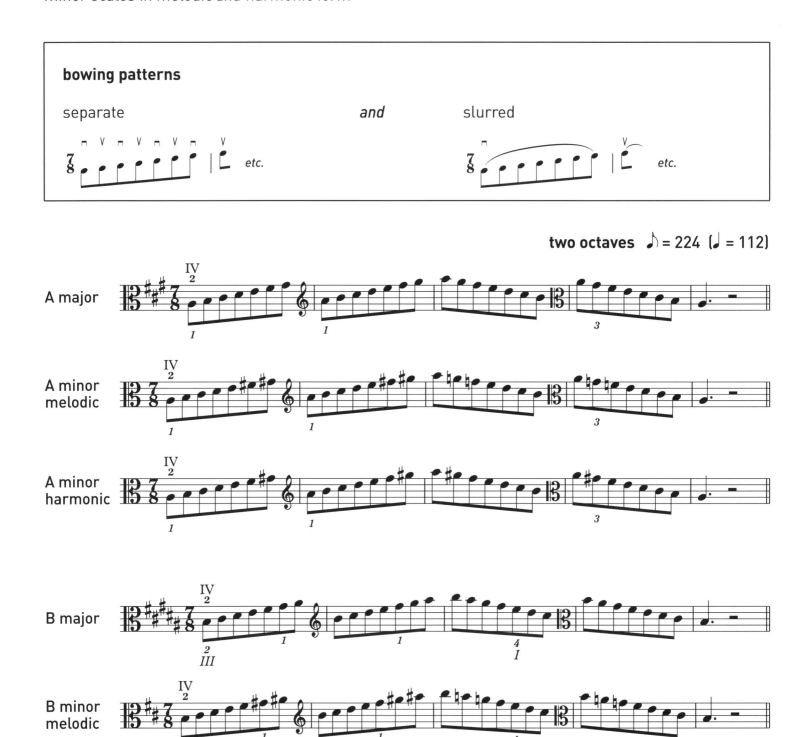

three octaves ♪ = 224 (♩ = 112)

Db major

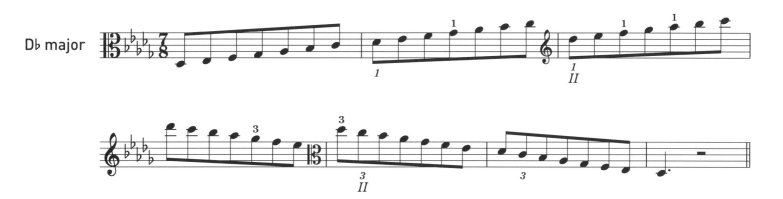

C# minor
melodic

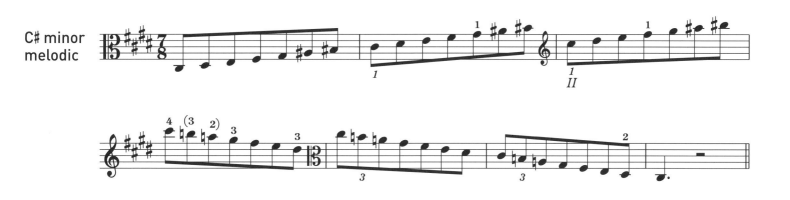

C# minor
harmonic

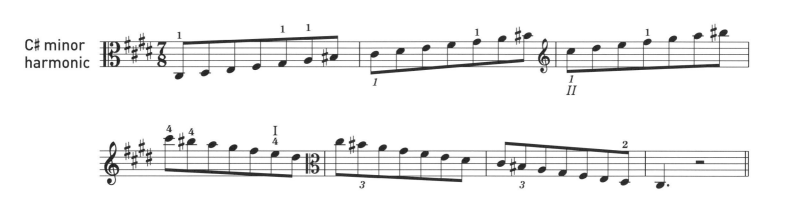

Eb major

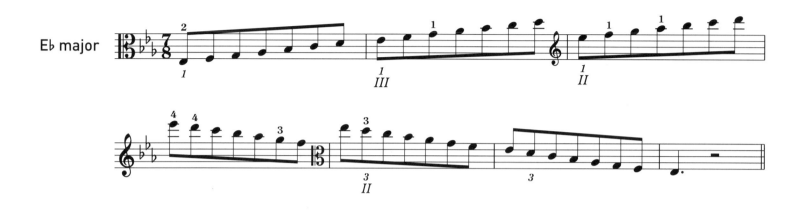

Eb minor
melodic

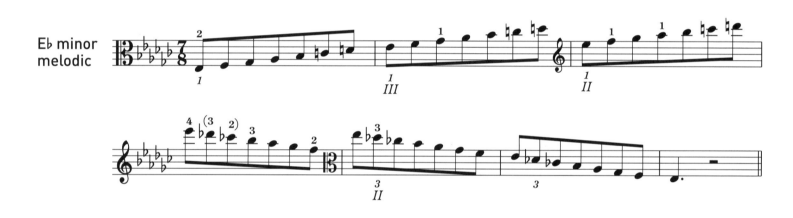

Eb minor
harmonic

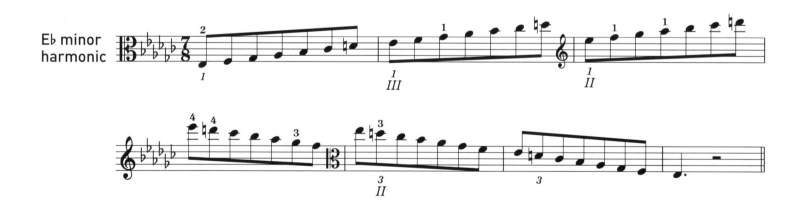

E major

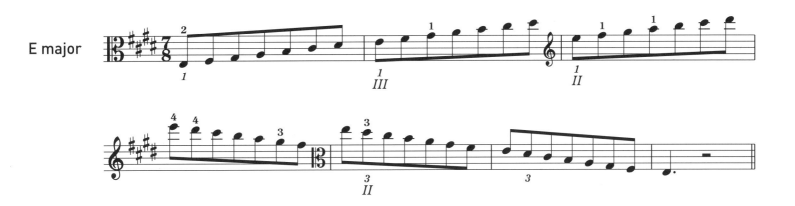

E minor melodic

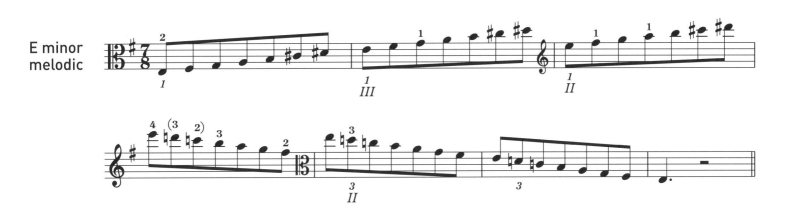

E minor harmonic

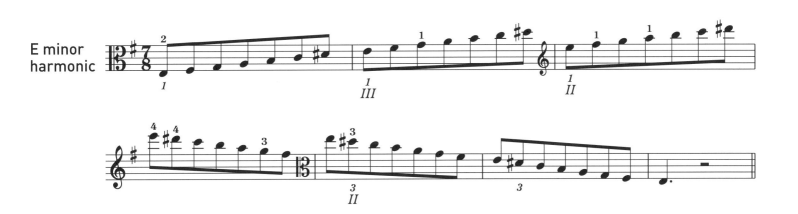

LONG TONIC

separate bows *and* slurred
minor scales in melodic *and* harmonic form

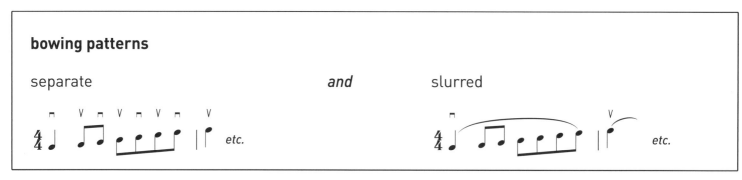

two octaves ♩ = 112

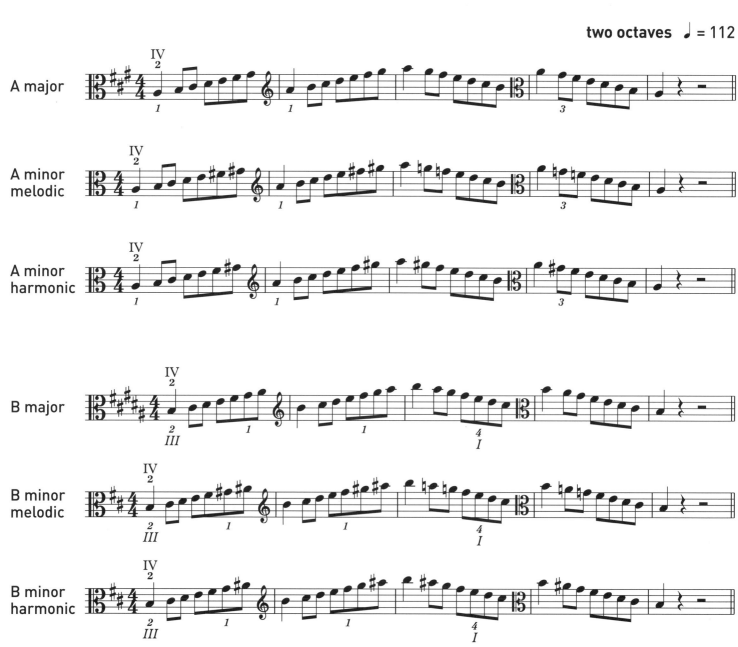

three octaves ♩ = 112

Db major

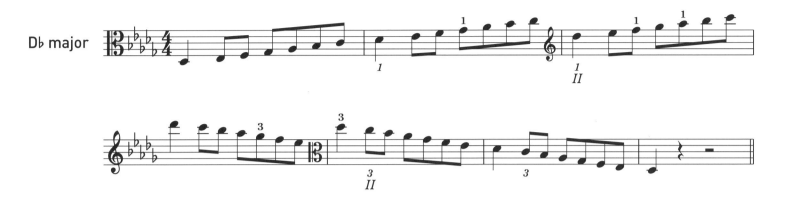

C# minor
melodic

C# minor
harmonic

Eb major

Eb minor melodic

Eb minor harmonic

E major

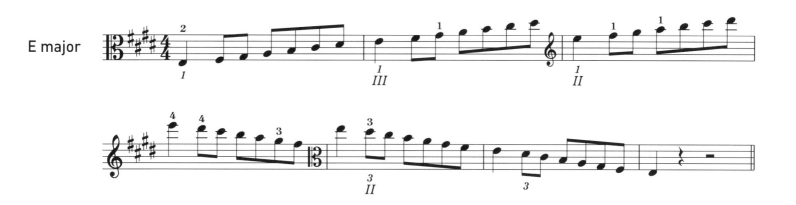

E minor
melodic

E minor
harmonic

ARPEGGIOS
separate bows *and* slurred

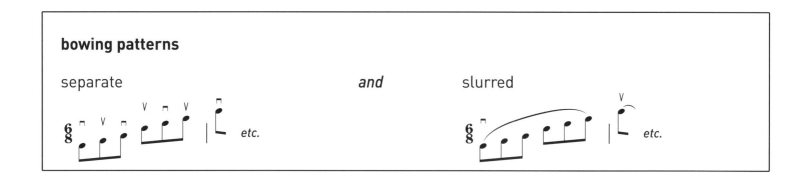

two octaves ♩. = 46

A major

A minor

B major
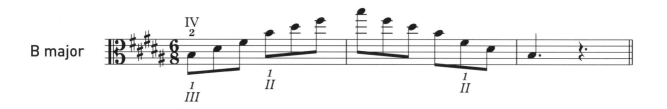

B minor

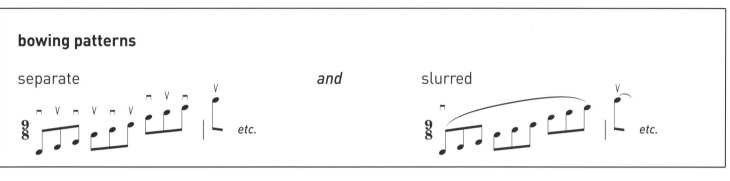

DOMINANT SEVENTHS
separate bows *and* slurred

bowing patterns

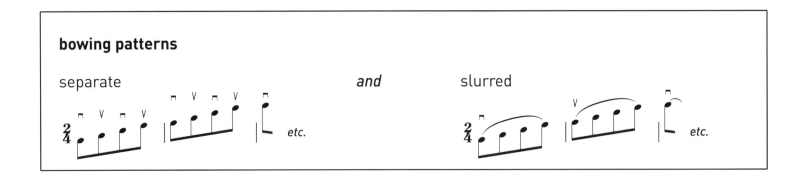

two octaves ♩ = 69

in the
key of D

three octaves ♩ = 69

in the
key of F♯

in the
key of A♭

in the
key of A

DIMINISHED SEVENTHS
separate bows *and* slurred

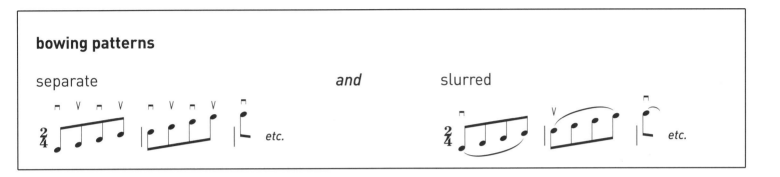

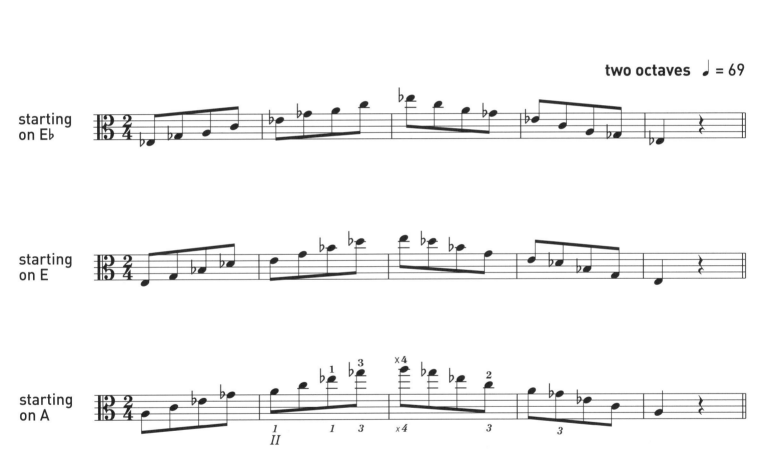

For practical purposes, the diminished sevenths are notated using some enharmonic equivalents.

CHROMATIC SCALES
separate bows *and* slurred

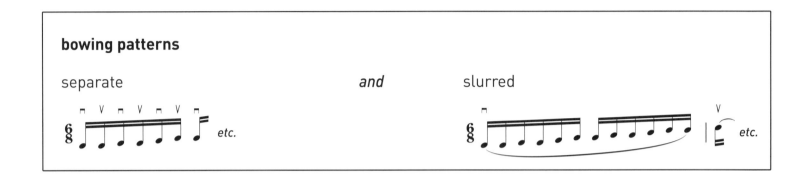

two octaves ♪ = 112

starting
on E♭

starting
on E

AB 3619

starting
on A

three octaves ♪ = 112

starting
on C♯

DOUBLE-STOP SCALES
IN PARALLEL even notes *or* long tonic at candidate's choice
EVEN NOTES

separate bows only
minor scale in melodic *and* harmonic form

one octave ♩ = 66

in octaves
in G major

in octaves
in C minor
melodic

in octaves
in C minor
harmonic

two octaves ♩ = 66

in sixths
in A♭ major

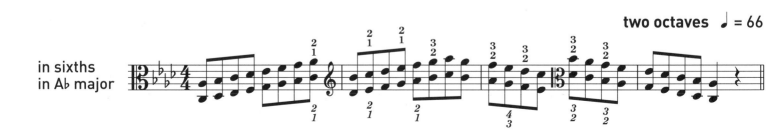

AB 3619

LONG TONIC

separate bows only
minor scale in melodic *and* harmonic form

bowing pattern

separate

one octave ♩ = 66

in octaves
in G major

in octaves
in C minor
melodic

in octaves
in C minor
harmonic

two octaves ♩ = 66

in sixths
in A♭ major

IN BROKEN STEPS

rhythm and bowing as shown

bowing pattern

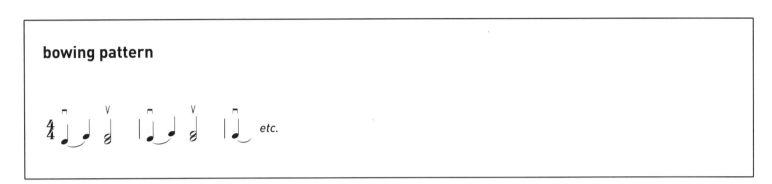

two octaves ♩ = 112

in thirds
in E♭ major